This book belongs to

...Karen.....Stevenson....3b.......

The Pumpkin book of
Nursery Rhymes

The Pumpkin book of Nursery Rhymes

PUMPKIN PRESS

First published in Great Britain in 1980 by
Pumpkin Press
113 Westbourne Grove London W2 4UP

Copyright © 1980 Pumpkin Press London

Illustrations copyright © 1980
Sandy Nightingale Mary Cartwright Kevin Maddison Marilyn Day

ISBN 0 906946 04 2

Colour reproduction by Culver Graphics Litho Ltd Bucks

Printed in Belgium by Henri Proost & CIE PVBA
Reprinted 1982

Rhymes in this book

Old Mother Goose
Baa baa black sheep
Wee Willie Winkie
Pussy cat, pussy cat
Handy Spandy, Jack-a-dandy
Barber, barber, shave a pig
Peter, Peter, pumpkin eater
Mary Mary quite contrary
Little Polly Flinders
Dear dear! What can the matter be?
Doctor Foster
Goosey goosey gander
Old Mother Hubbard
Sing sing what shall I sing?
Little Bo-Peep
Molly my sister, and I fell out
Jerry Hall
Who killed Cock Robin?
Little Jack Horner
How many miles to Babylon?
Lucy Locket
Little maid, pretty maid
The Man in the Moon
What is the news of the day?

Hey diddle diddle
Jack and Jill went up the hill
A wise old owl
I know I have lost my train
As I went to Bonner
Twinkle twinkle little star
Little Poll Parrot
There was an old woman
Four and twenty tailors
A cat came fiddling out of a barn
One, two, three, four, five
Humpty Dumpty sat on a wall
In the greenhouse lives a wren
Georgie Porgie pudding and pie
Where O where has my little dog gone?
Hickety pickety my fine hen
Hickory dickory dock
Ding dong bell
There was an old crow
Round and round the garden
There was a rat
Diddlety diddlety dumpty
I had a little hobby horse
Jack be nimble, Jack be quick

Old Mother Goose,
When she wanted to wander,
Would ride through the air
On a very fine gander.

Baa, baa, black sheep,
Have you any wool?
Yes sir, yes sir,
Three bags full;
One for the master,
And one for the dame,
And one for the little boy
Who lives down the lane.

Wee Willie Winkie
Runs through the town,
Upstairs and downstairs, in his nightgown;
Rapping at the windows, crying through
   the lock,
Are the children all in bed, for now
   it's eight o'clock?

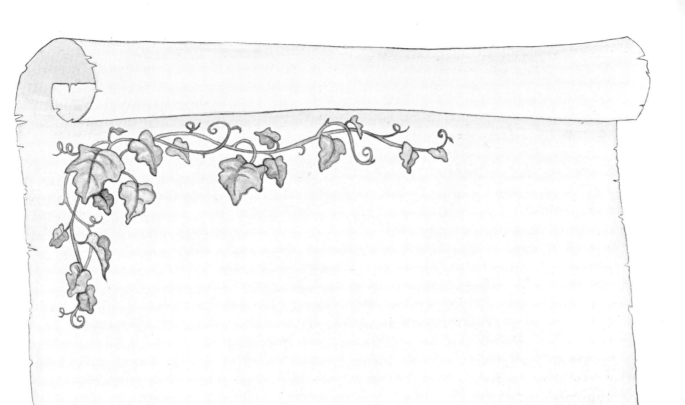

Pussy cat, pussy cat, where have you been?
I've been to London to look at the queen.
Pussy cat, pussy cat, what did you there?
I frightened a little mouse under her chair.

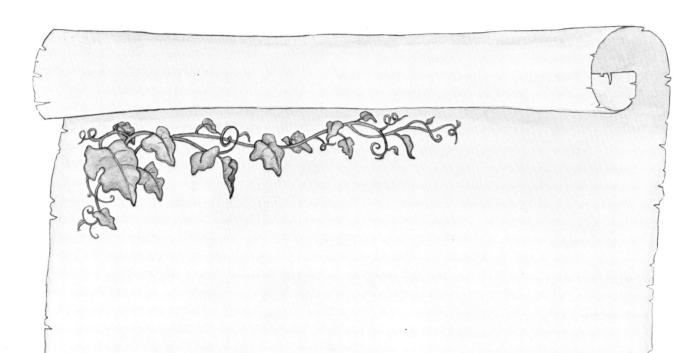

Handy Spandy, Jack-a-dandy
Loves plum cake and sugar candy.
He bought some at the grocer's shop
And out he came, hop, hop, hop.

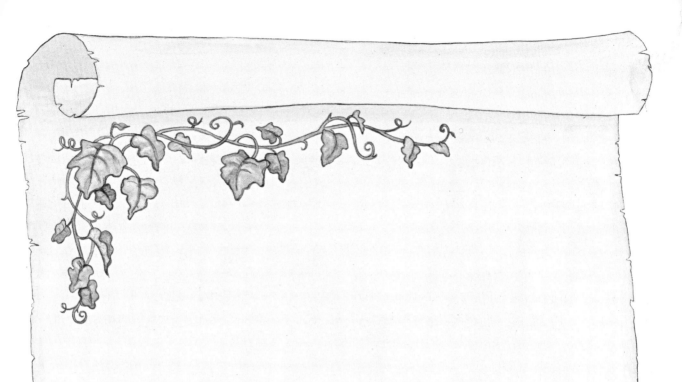

Barber, barber, shave a pig,
How many hairs to make a wig?
Four and twenty, that's enough.
Give the barber a pinch of snuff.

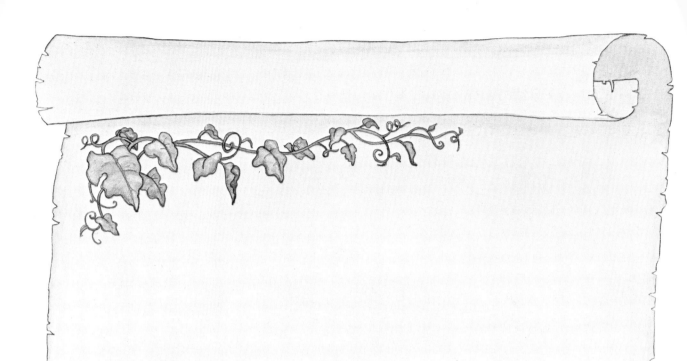

Peter, Peter, pumpkin-eater
Had a wife and couldn't keep her;
He put her in a pumpkin shell,
And there he kept her very well.

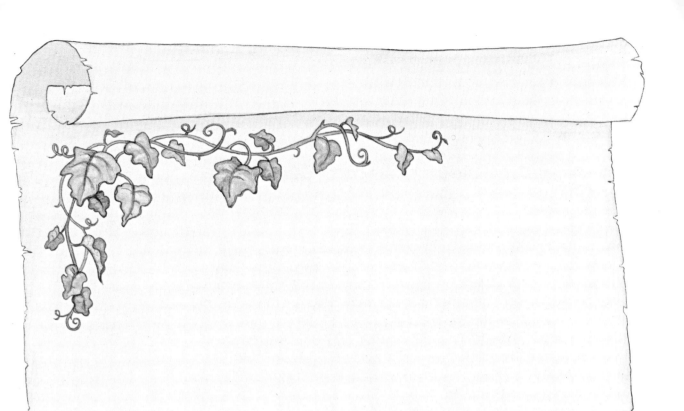

Mary, Mary, quite contrary,
How does your garden grow?
With silver bells and cockle shells
And pretty maids all in a row.

Little Polly Flinders
Sat among the cinders,
Warming her pretty little toes;
Her mother came and caught her,
And whipped her little daughter,
For spoiling her nice new clothes.

Dear, dear! What can the matter be?
Two old women got up in an apple tree;
One came down and the other stayed
  till Saturday.

Doctor Foster
Went to Gloucester
In a shower of rain;
He stepped in a puddle
Right up to his middle,
And never went there again.

Goosey, goosey gander,
Wither shall I wander?
Upstairs and downstairs
And in my lady's chamber.
There I met an old man
Who would not say his prayers,
I took him by the left leg
And threw him down the stairs.

Old Mother Hubbard
Went to the cupboard
To fetch her poor dog a bone;
But when she got there
The cupboard was bare,
And so the poor dog had none.

Sing, sing, what shall I sing?
The cat's run away with the pudding-string!
Do, do, what shall I do?
The cat has bitten it quite in two.

Little Bo-Peep
Has lost her sheep,
And can't tell where to find them;
Leave them alone, and they'll come home,
Bringing their tails behind them.

Molly, my sister, and I fell out,
And what do you think it was all about?
She loved coffee and I loved tea.
And that was the reason we couldn't agree.

Jerry Hall
He was so small,
A rat could eat him,
Hat and all.

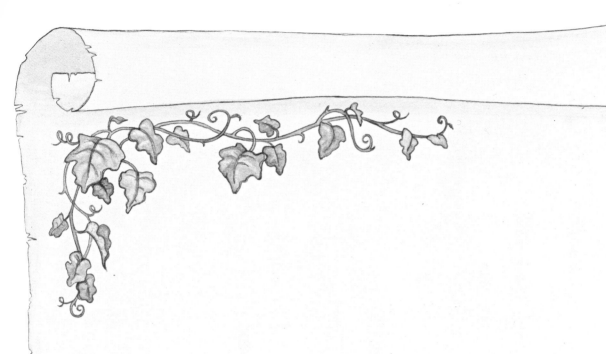

Who killed Cock Robin?
I, said the sparrow,
With my bow and arrow,
I killed Cock Robin.

Little Jack Horner
Sat in the corner,
Eating a Christmas pie;
He put in his thumb, and pulled out a plum,
And said, what a good boy am I!

How many miles to Babylon?
Threescore miles and ten.
Can I get there by candlelight?
Yes, and back again.
If your heels be nimble and light,
You may get there by candlelight.

Lucy Locket
Lost her pocket,
Kitty Fisher found it;
There was not a penny in it,
But a ribbon round it.

Little maid, pretty maid, whither goest thou?
Down in the meadow to milk my cow.
Shall I go with thee?
No, not now;
When I send for thee, then come thou.

The Man in the Moon
Came down too soon,
And asked his way to Norwich;
He went by the South,
And burnt his mouth
With eating cold plum porridge.

What is the news of the day,
Good neighbour, I pray?
They say the balloon
Is gone up to the moon!

Hey diddle diddle, the cat and the fiddle,
The cow jumped over the moon;
The little dog laughed
To see such sport,
And the dish ran away with the spoon.

Jack and Jill went up the hill
To fetch a pail of water;
Jack fell down and broke his crown,
And Jill came tumbling after.

A wise old owl sat in an oak,
The more he heard the less he spoke;
The less he spoke the more he heard.
Why aren't we all like that wise old bird?

I know I have lost my train,
Said a man named Joshua Lane;
But I'll run on the rails
With my coat-tails for sails,
And maybe I'll catch it again.

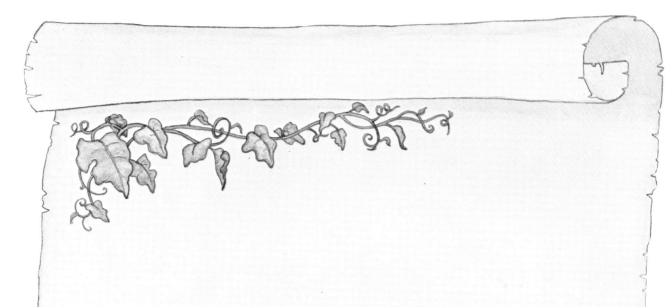

As I went to Bonner,
I met a pig
Without a wig,
Upon my word and honour.

Twinkle, twinkle, little star,
How I wonder what you are!
Up above the world so high,
Like a diamond in the sky.

Little Poll Parrot
Sat in his garret,
Eating toast and tea;
A little brown mouse
Jumped into his house,
And stole it all away.

There was an old woman
   who lived in a shoe,
She had so many children
   she didn't know what to do.
She gave them some broth
   without any bread,
And whipped them all soundly
   and put them to bed.

Four and twenty tailors went to kill a snail,
The best man amongst them durst not
    touch her tail;
She put out her horns like a little
    Kyloe cow,
Run, tailors, run, or she'll kill you all
    e'en now.

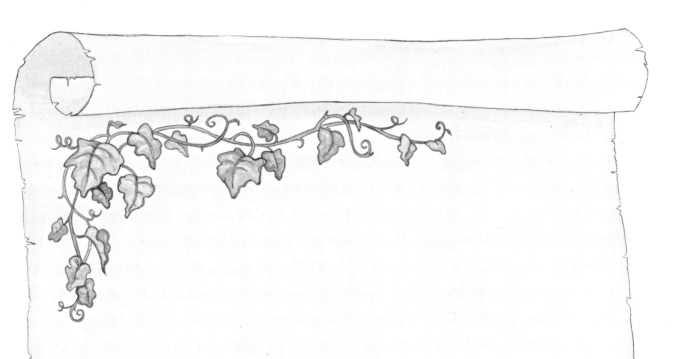

A cat came fiddling out of a barn,
With a pair of bagpipes under her arm;
She could sing nothing but fiddle-de-dee,
The mouse has married the bumble bee.
Pipe, cat; dance, mouse;
We'll have a wedding at our good house.

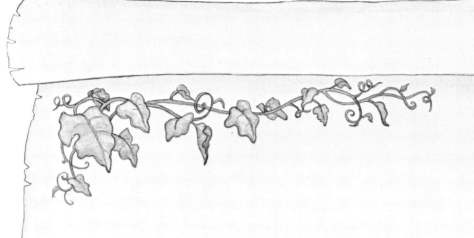

One, two, three, four, five,
Once I caught a fish alive.
Six, seven, eight, nine, ten,
Then I let it go again.
Why did you let it go?
Because it bit my finger so.
Which finger did it bite?
The little finger on the right.

Humpty Dumpty sat on a wall,
Humpty Dumpty had a great fall;
All the king's horses and all the king's men
Couldn't put Humpty together again.

In the greenhouse lives a wren,
Little friend of little men;
When they're good she tells them where
To find the apple, quince and pear.

Georgie Porgie, pudding and pie,
Kissed the girls and made them cry;
When the boys came out to play,
Georgie Porgie ran away.

Where, O where, has my little dog gone?
O where, O where, can he be?
With his tail cut short, and his ears cut long,
O where, O where, is he?

Hickety, pickety, my fine hen,
She lays eggs for gentlemen;
Gentlemen come every day
To see what my fine hen doth lay.
Sometimes nine and sometimes ten,
Hickety, pickety, my fine hen.

Hickory, dickory, dock
The mouse ran up the clock;
The clock struck one,
The mouse ran down,
Hickory, dickory, dock.

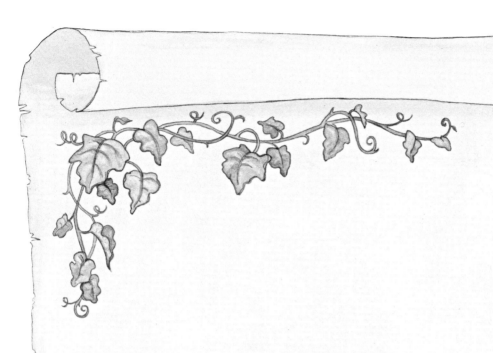

Ding, dong, bell,
Pussy's in the well.
Who put her in?
Little Johnny Green.
Who pulled her out?
Little Tommy Stout.
What a naughty boy was that
To try to drown poor pussy cat,
Which never did him any harm,
But killed the mice in his father's barn.

There was an old crow
Sat upon a clod;
That's the end of my song.
That's odd.

Round and round the garden
Like a teddy bear;
One step, two step,
Tickle you under there!

There was a rat,
For want of stairs,
Went down a rope
To say his prayers.

Diddlety, diddlety, dumpty,
The cat ran up the plum tree;
Half a crown to fetch her down,
Diddlety, diddlety, dumpty.

I had a little hobby-horse,
And it was dapple grey,
Its head was made of pea-straw,
Its tail was made of hay.

I sold it to an old woman
For a copper groat;
And I'll not sing my song again
Without another coat.

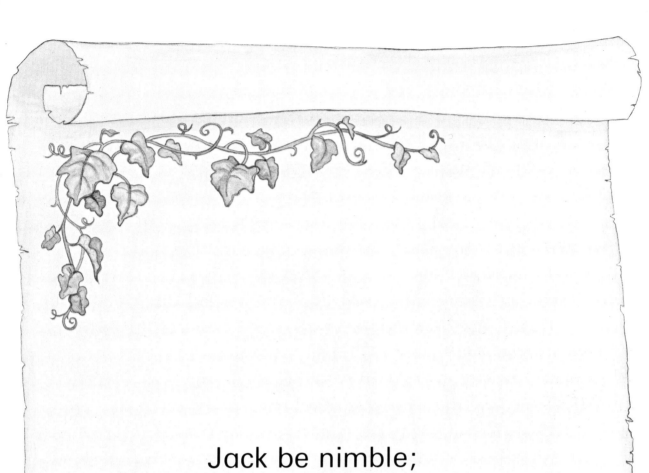

Jack be nimble;
Jack be quick;
Jack jump over
The candlestick.